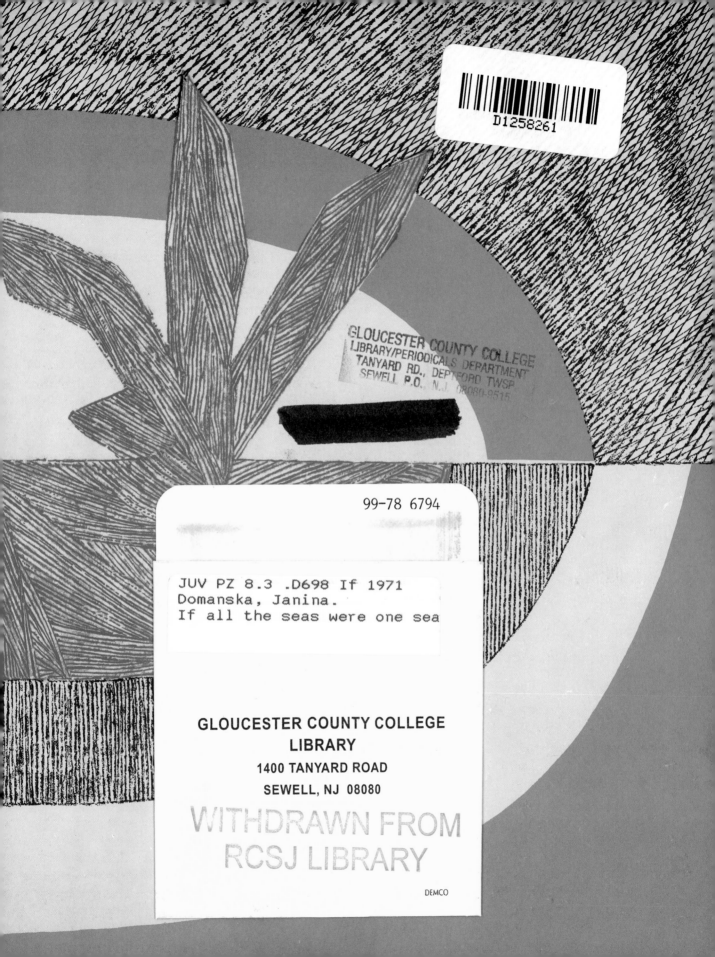

IF ALL THE SEAS WERE ONE SEA

ETCHINGS BY JANINA DOMANSKA

THE MACMILLAN COMPANY, NEW YORK

COLLIER-MACMILLAN LTD., LONDON

12783

The Macmillan Company, 866 Third Avenue, New York, N.Y. 10022
Collier-Macmillan Canada Ltd., Toronto, Ontario
Library of Congress catalog card number: 73-146621
Printed in the United States of America

1 2 3 4 5 6 7 8 9 10

The art was prepared in four colors—etchings on zinc plates for
blue and black and brush-and-ink overlays for red and green.
The typeface is Weiss roman, with display lettering etched by the artist.

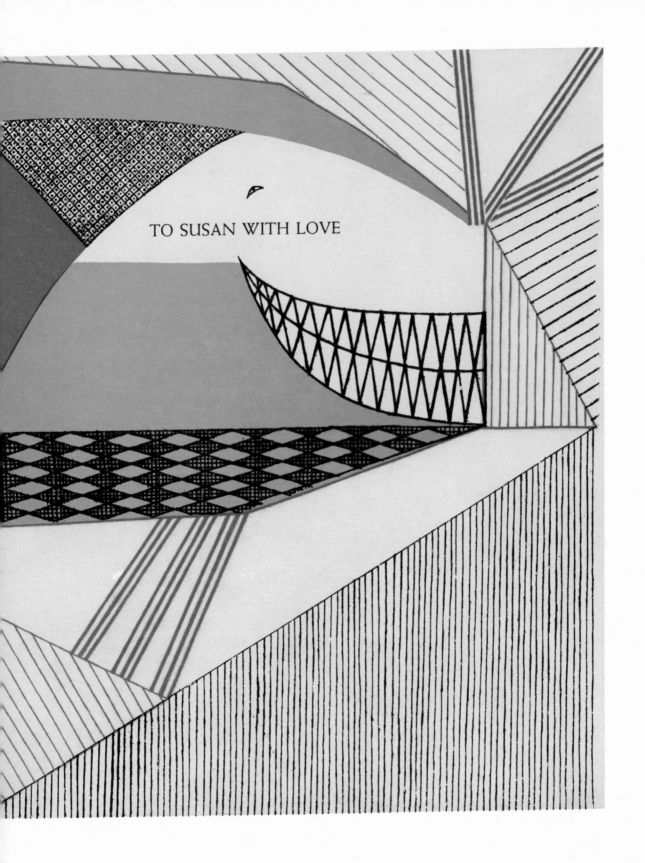

TO SUSAN WITH LOVE

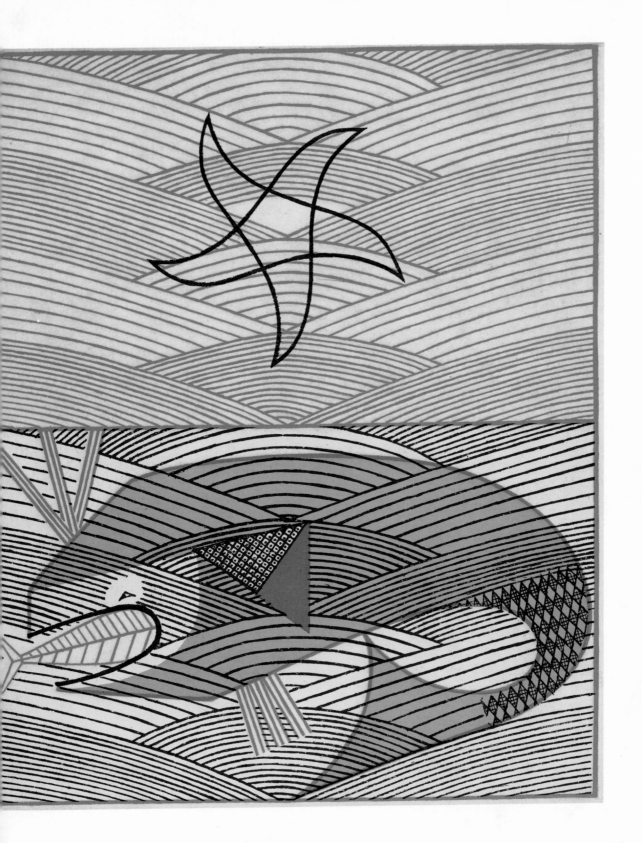

If all the seas were one sea,

what a great sea that would be.

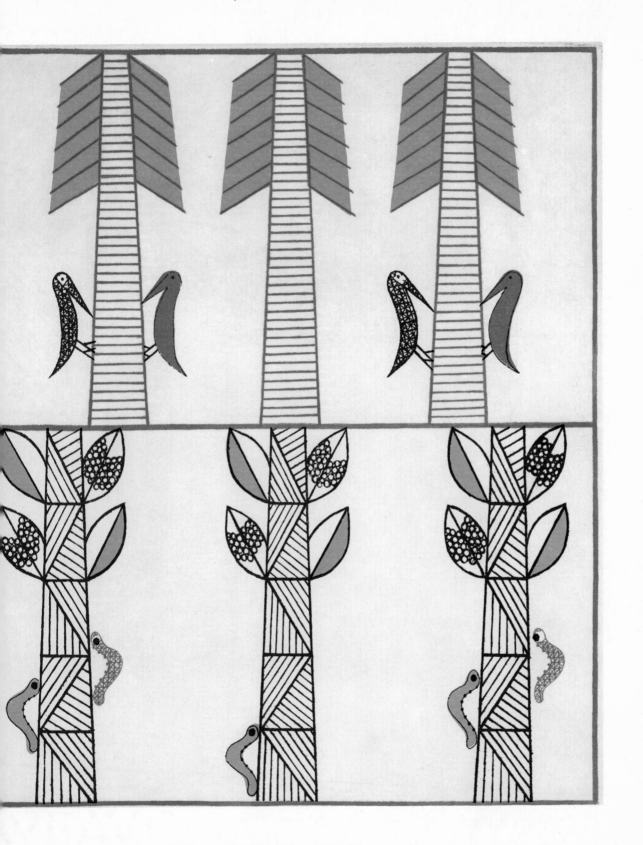

And if all the trees were one tree,

what a great tree that would be.

And if all the axes were one ax,

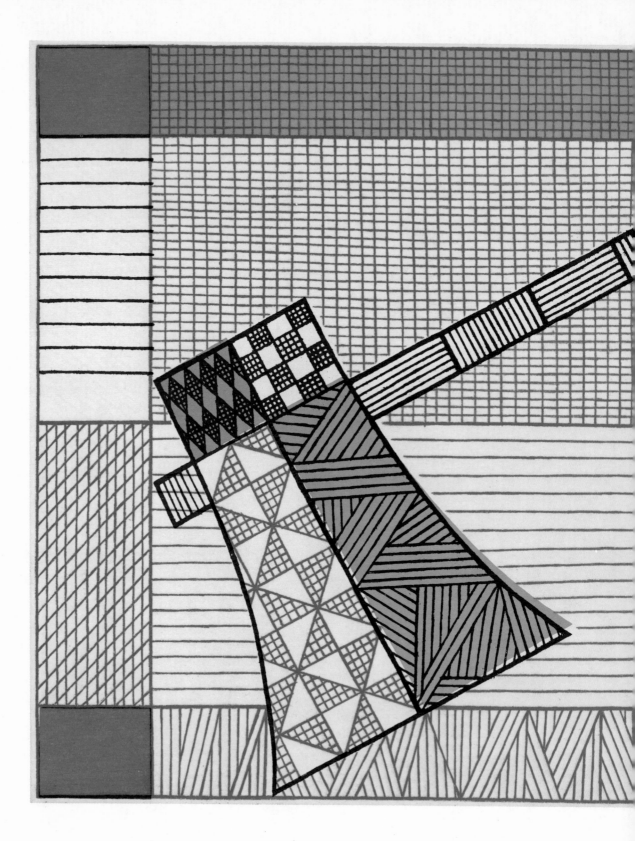

what a great ax that would be.

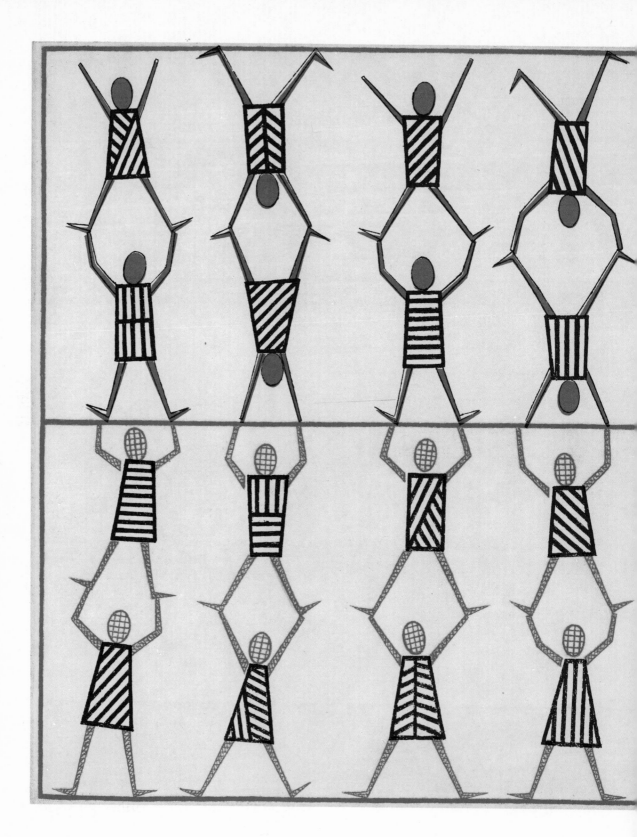

And if all the men were one man,

what a great man that would be.

And if the great man

took the great ax

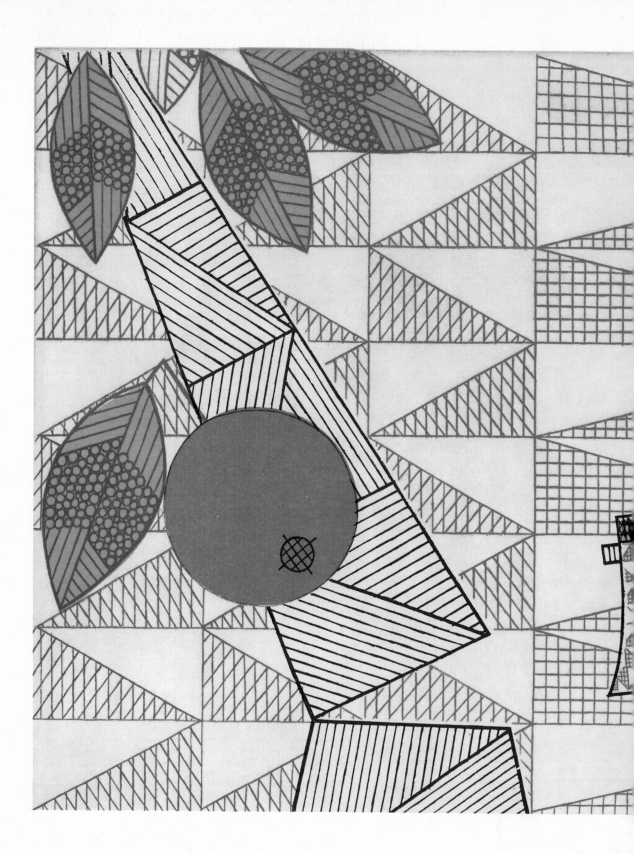

and cut down the great tree

and let it fall

into the great sea,

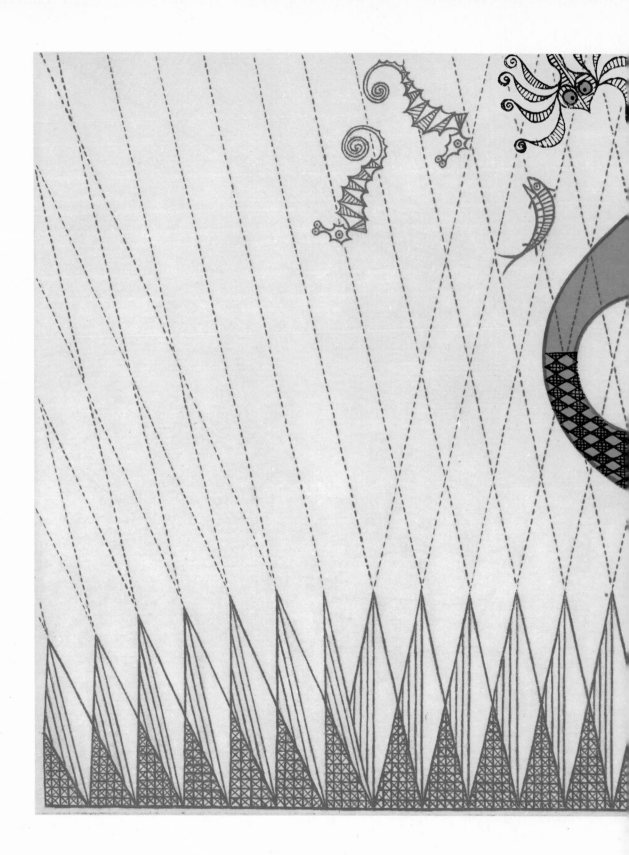

what a splish splash that would be!